The Childhood of Famous Americans Series

BY WILLIAM O. STEELE

JOHN SEVIER: *Pioneer Boy*

BY AUGUSTA STEVENSON

ABE LINCOLN: *Frontier Boy*
BEN FRANKLIN: *Printer's Boy*
ANDY JACKSON: *Boy Soldier*
GEORGE WASHINGTON: *Boy Leader*
DANIEL BOONE: *Boy Hunter*
SAM HOUSTON: *Boy Chieftain*
GEORGE CARVER: *Boy Scientist*
KIT CARSON: *Boy Trapper*
PAUL REVERE: *Boy of Old Boston*
CLARA BARTON: *Girl Nurse*
U. S. GRANT: *Young Horseman*
BUFFALO BILL: *Boy of the Plains*
ANTHONY WAYNE: *Daring Boy*
MYLES STANDISH:
  Adventurous Boy
BOOKER T. WASHINGTON:
  Ambitious Boy
WILBUR AND ORVILLE WRIGHT:
  Boys with Wings
MOLLY PITCHER: *Girl Patriot*

BY GUERNSEY VAN RIPER, JR.

LOU GEHRIG: *Boy of the Sand Lots*
WILL ROGERS: *Young Cowboy*
KNUTE ROCKNE: *Young Athlete*

BY JEAN BROWN WAGONER

LOUISA ALCOTT:
  Girl of Old Boston

BY JEAN BROWN WAGONER—*cont.*

JANE ADDAMS: *Little Lame Girl*
JULIA WARD HOWE:
  Girl of Old New York
MARTHA WASHINGTON:
  Girl of Old Virginia
ABIGAIL ADAMS:
  A Girl of Colonial Days

BY ANN WEIL

JOHN QUINCY ADAMS:
  Boy Patriot
FRANKLIN ROOSEVELT:
  Boy of the Four Freedoms

BY MABEL CLELAND WIDDEMER

WASHINGTON IRVING:
  Boy of Old New York
ALECK BELL: *Ingenious Boy*
HARRIET BEECHER STOWE:
  Connecticut Girl
PETER STUYVESANT:
  Boy with Wooden Shoes

BY KATHARINE E. WILKIE

ZACK TAYLOR:
  Young Rough and Ready

BY GERTRUDE HECKER WINDERS

JAMES FENIMORE COOPER:
  Leatherstocking Boy
JIM BOWIE:
  Boy with a Hunting Knife

The Childhood of Famous American

LOUISA ALCOTT

Girl of Old Boston

LOUISA ALCOTT
Girl of Old Boston

BY
Jean Brown Wagoner

ILLUSTRATED BY
Sandra James

THE BOBBS-MERRILL COMPANY
Publishers

INDIANAPOLIS   NEW YORK

CONTENTS

FULL-PAGE ILLUSTRATIONS

I

LOUISA

IT WAS unusually quiet in the Alcott home. Father was in his study, writing. Mother was in the nursery with baby Elizabeth, and Anna and Louisa were in their playroom. Suddenly there was a terrific noise. Father rushed from the study. Anna and Louisa were screaming at the top of their lungs. He ran to the playroom. "What is the matter?"

The two little girls were fighting each other like wildcats. "Children! Children! This is no way for sisters to act."

"She won't give me the rocking chair!" shrieked Louisa.

"It's mine!"

"I was in it first!"

"You weren't either!"

"Was too."

The two little girls were fighting each other like wildcats.

"Wait, wait," broke in Father. "Anna, you're the older, don't you think you should give up the chair to your younger sister?"

"I always have to give up," wailed Anna. "She pinched me, too."

"You come into the study with me. We'll

She sat in front of the fire and waited.

leave Louisa in here by herself. Maybe if she thinks about it she'll be sorry and let you have the chair."

Anna went with Father. She sat in front of the fire and waited. But Louisa didn't call. She kept the chair all afternoon.

"We must help Louisa control her temper," said Father that evening. "She's nearly three years old and grows naughtier every day."

"I have tried every way I know to correct her," sighed Mother. "I have talked to her and scolded her, and whipped her, even. The other day I shut her up in a dark closet. She thought that was great fun and begged me today to shut her up again. I don't know what to try next."

"I'll take her to school. Perhaps that will help." So Father took Louisa to school before she was three years old.

All this happened in Boston many years ago, in 1835. The Alcotts were well known there.

Father was a famous schoolmaster. Mother had grown up there. Louisa was well known, too, but for a different reason. She was always in trouble. From the time she could crawl she had been in mischief.

Once, before she was two, she was lost on board a ship. Her father and mother and everybody thought she had fallen overboard. They

If things were too quiet, she pulled the covers off the tables.

found her at last in the engine room, black and dirty and covered with grease.

Louisa wanted something going on all the time. If things were too quiet, she pulled the covers off the tables. She had learned that all kinds of things happened then.

She was always asking questions. If her mother was busy and didn't answer her, she ran to the cradle where the baby was asleep and cried, "I'll wake the baby!"

Now that she was nearly three it was high time she learned to mend her ways.

Father took Louisa to the school which he taught. They didn't have far to go. It was close by.

Most schools were ugly. The children sat on hard wooden benches. The walls and windows were black with smoke from the stove. There were no pictures, no story books, and no geographies with colored maps. The teacher was usually a cross old man with a whip in his hand. When the children didn't learn their lessons, he used the whip.

Louisa's father was not like that. He was always pleasant and never used a whip. He loved children and loved to teach them.

Louisa liked the schoolroom. It was warm and pretty. The windows were like those in a church. The walls were painted. The floor was covered with beautiful rugs. There were fine pictures and books all around the room.

There was no other school like this. People heard about it. They came from far and near to visit it. They couldn't believe their eyes. "The boys and girls of Mr. Alcott's school love to study," they said. "Whoever heard of such a thing? They learn faster than any other children in the country."

Many rich people sent their children to Mr.

Alcott. They paid him a great deal of money. He bought more books and fine statues.

Mr. Alcott taught the children to read and write and spell. He taught them more than that. He taught them to be kind to one another and to love beautiful things. They were happy.

The people of Boston were proud of Mr. Alcott and his school. Louisa's mother was wise to send her there.

II

THE FIRST LESSON

IN THE evenings after school, between teatime and supper, Father worked in his study. He was writing a book about Anna and Elizabeth and Louisa. Each day he wrote down what they were doing.

Louisa liked to sit on the floor beside her father and pretend to write, too. She wrote busily in all the books within reach. Other times she played with the big, heavy books as if they were blocks, and built towers and walls and bridges with them. If a book opened at a picture, she took it to her father and laid it on his knee.

"Read this to Weezie," she would say.

"After supper, Louisa, not now," he would reply.

One evening Louisa marched over to her

father. She pushed his pen away and with her hands covered the page on which he was writing. "Read now, not after," she demanded crossly.

Father looked serious. He held one of her hands down on the paper. Then he took a pencil and carefully drew a line around the little fist. When she took her hand away, there was the outline of it on the page. Father wrote beneath it, "Louisa's hand."

"It doesn't look like a bad little hand, does it?" he said.

"It isn't bad. It's a good hand and 'longs to Weezie," said Louisa sturdily.

"But I saw it push Father's hand away just now, so he couldn't work. That was bad," said Mr. Alcott. "Today I saw it pinch somebody, like this." He pinched Louisa's cheek hard. She didn't cry, but her lips trembled and her eyes were big with tears.

"That hurt, didn't it?" he asked. Louisa nodded. "Was it nice of me to do that to you?"

"No, that wasn't fair," said Louisa.

"Do you know why I did it?"

" 'Cause Weezie did it to Anna."

"Had Anna hurt you?"

Louisa hung her head. "No," she whispered.

"Then that wasn't fair either, was it?" The little girl stood ashamed and silent.

"What shall we do to make this hand kind and gentle?"

"Cut it off?" suggested Louisa, hiding her hand behind her.

"No, no," replied Father. "It couldn't do anything then, could it?"

Louisa thought a moment, then spoke brightly. "Weezie can play she's Mother, then her hands will be soft."

"Why, that is the very thing," agreed Father

happily. "No one's hands are busier or kinder than Mother's. Why is that?"

"'Cause Mother's more kinder than anybody," came the answer.

"Always remember that, little daughter. When you're angry and want to pinch someone or throw something, just say to yourself, 'Mother wouldn't do that.' It will help you guide your hands."

Later in the evening, as soon as supper was over, Louisa opened her story book to her favorite picture and ran with it to Father. "Now read," she said, and pushed the book into his hands. Anna had brought a book too, and gave it to him at the same time.

Louisa pushed her back and said, "Read mine first."

"I was here first," said Anna.

Louisa jumped at Anna. "I'll pinch you," she scolded, and then stopped herself. She turned and smiled at Father. "Weezie forgot." Then she picked up Anna's book and gave it to him.

He was so pleased that he took her by the hands and danced a jig with her. Around and around the room they pranced. Anna and

Around and around the room they pranced.

Mother looked on in astonishment, then they joined in too. Lizzie clapped her hands.

"This is fun," thought Louisa. "I'm going to be good all the time."

"Louisa has learned her first lesson," thought Father.

III

LOUISA HAS A BIRTHDAY PARTY

L OUISA lay in bed thinking. "I'm going to be as good as I can be today. This is my birthday. I'll be four years old and I'm going to have a party."

She jumped out of bed. Then she hopped back in again. The floor was icy cold. It was snowing outside.

Louisa heard Father making a fire in the fireplace downstairs. There were fireplaces in every room. At night Father would cover the fires with ashes. In the morning he poked them and uncovered the red-hot embers. He piled on fresh wood. Soon the fires would be blazing and the rooms would be warm.

Today Louisa was too excited to lie still and wait for a fire. She jumped up again and ran to the washstand in the corner of the room.

Louisa tipped the pitcher to pour water into the basin. No water ran out. She looked inside. A film of ice was over the top of the water.

"Oh goody!" she cried. "I love cold water." She broke the ice, poured the water, and washed and splashed to her heart's content.

She broke the ice and poured the water.

By that time she felt so lively she had to have someone to play with. She looked over at Anna. Anna was still in bed. Louisa took a piece of ice and let it trickle down Anna's neck.

"Ow!" squealed Anna, and hid her head under the pillow. Then began a tug of war. Louisa pulled one end of the pillow. Anna pulled the other. Suddenly Anna let go. Louisa went tumbling head over heels.

Mother called upstairs. "No time for play this morning. Have you forgotten what day this is, Louisa?"

Louisa hurried into her clothes and ran downstairs. She hugged her mother and danced around her father. She ran to the kitchen to see what Cook had for breakfast. Louisa loved breakfast in the winter. The applesauce and the muffins and the cereal smelled good. It seemed to her that the rest of the family never would be ready to sit down. She ran outdoors and played in the snow till Cook called her.

As soon as breakfast was over, Anna and Louisa ran back upstairs and made their beds. This was not easy to do. The sheets were as cold as ice and made their fingers numb. They made their room neat, then went back downstairs to run errands for Mother. After that, Anna got out her books to study a little before school. Louisa didn't get out her books. She didn't have to go to school on her birthday.

Soon Father and Anna left for school. Louisa went into the library and played with her Father's books.

Mother brought in the cradle and let Lizzie watch Louisa at her play. Louisa peeked at her now and then. Baby tried to reach her through the sides of the cradle.

Louisa decided to let her play with the books, too. She lifted her out of the cradle and set her

down in the midst of the books. She built towers
and let Lizzie topple them over with her foot.

Then Louisa built a wall around her. At first
it was a little low wall, but Louisa made it higher
and higher. Finally, it was so high that she
couldn't see over it. She looked at Baby through
a crack. Lizzie lay there quite still looking all
about. Then she spied Louisa at the crack. She
clapped her hands and laughed out loud.

Louisa played peek-a-boo with her for a long
time. After a while she pulled a heavy piece of
wrapping paper over the top of the wall. That
made it so dark inside she couldn't see Lizzie.
She waited to see what would happen. She
thought: "Maybe Baby won't like this new
game. Maybe she thinks she is in a dark prison
or something."

While she was waiting, Mother called. "Louisa, would you like to watch me make the cakes
for your birthday party?" Away Louisa flew.

She forgot all about Lizzie and the paper and the books.

In the kitchen Mother was ready to begin. She had scooped the sugar from the barrel. It was hard and lumpy and yellow. Mother put the sugar in a heavy cloth bag. Then she took the hammer and pounded it to break up the lumps. She poured the sugar onto the bread board and rolled and rolled it with the rolling pin until it was soft and fine. She creamed the sugar and butter together, then stirred in the eggs and flour and milk until she had a smooth batter.

Louisa stood at the window sill and leaned her elbows on the kitchen table and watched. Every now and then she stuck her finger into the bowl and took a taste. My, but it was good!

When the little cakes were all baked and iced, Mother let Louisa sprinkle them with red sugar. They were the prettiest cakes Louisa had ever seen.

"Now, I must feed little Lizzie," said Mother. "She has finished her nap by this time." Mother ran in to lift the baby from the cradle. When she got there, she cried out. "Why, where is she? Where is my baby?"

She threw the covers back. She looked under the cradle. She looked about the room. There was no baby in sight. Louisa heard Mother and came running.

"Oh, Louisa, I can't find Lizzie."

Louisa's mind was full of pretty red-sugared cakes. She hardly heard her mother. She followed her about while Mother rushed from room to room. Cook joined the search. No Lizzie was to be found. Mother was out of breath and frightened.

All at once Louisa remembered. "Oh, I know where Lizzie is. She's in a big black dungeon." The cook shrieked.

Mother took Louisa by the hand. "Quick, Louisa. Show me where she is."

Louisa led them back to the library. She pointed to the tower of books. "There she is," she said.

Mother rushed over and pulled the paper away. She was about to scold Louisa soundly for this prank, but inside the tower little Elizabeth lay fast asleep. She opened her eyes. She saw Louisa peeking at her. She thought they were still playing. She laughed so merrily that Mother didn't have the heart to scold. Her sleep on the floor inside the wall hadn't hurt her a bit.

Mother explained to Louisa later that it wasn't a safe place to leave their precious baby. Louisa didn't ever do it again.

Mother was nearly as glad as Louisa was when it was time for her to dress for the party.

"You will have to stand still, Louisa, or I can't button your dress," said Mother. "Don't you

want the party to begin? The children are waiting for you at the school."

Then Louisa hugged herself tight and stood
still. Mother tied a pink ribbon in Louisa's hair
and put a pink sash around her waist. Then they
went to the school.

They danced around her and sang "Happy Birthday."

When the children saw Louisa, they danced around her and sang "Happy Birthday, Happy Birthday." Anna ran to her and hugged her. Then Father called out, "Follow the leader," and the fun began. He played the leader and everybody fell in line behind him. He led them in all kinds of funny exercises. He jumped over his desk. He turned handsprings. He climbed in and out of the windows. The older boys had to help Louisa over the desk and lift her in and out of the windows, but she turned handsprings better than anybody. They played "Drop the Handkerchief" and "Spin the Plate." All at once it was time for refreshments.

Louisa's father called her to him. He lifted her onto a table. The children lined up in front of her. One of the girls put a crown on her head. They all sang a song they had learned just for her. Then Mother brought in the cakes. My, how the children clapped their hands when they saw them!

Louisa passed one to each guest. She could hardly wait to come to the end of the line. How fast the cakes disappeared! Oh, dear me, they were going too fast! Louisa looked at her mother.

"There aren't enough to go round," she whispered.

"Oh, surely there are," replied Mother, and she counted too.

Louisa was right. There was one cake short. Louisa came to the last guest, a little boy. There was only one cake left. Louisa covered it with her hand and wouldn't pass it. The little boy stood waiting.

"It is my party," she said to herself. "I ought to have a cake more than anybody."

Mother put her arms around Louisa. "It is always best to give away the nice things," she said. "I'm sure my Louisa won't let her little friend go without."

Then Louisa gave the boy the last little cake. Mother gave Louisa a kiss.

IV

LETTERS TELL STORIES

"I DON'T like letters. I wish they had never been born," sighed Louisa one night. She was studying her reading lesson for the next day. All the Alcotts were in the living room as usual. Supper was over and the fun of the day was about to begin. Father had a new story to read, and Anna and Louisa were going to act out a little play about King Midas and the Golden Touch.

They were all waiting for Louisa to finish.

"You don't really mean that you don't like letters," said Father. "You like stories, and letters tell stories."

"They don't tell me anything." Louisa made a face at the letter S. She had trouble remembering it.

Father wrote the letter on her slate. "What does it look like?" he asked.

"A wiggle-worm," replied Louisa.

"What is another thing that crawls along the ground?" Father got down and wriggled along the floor. He hissed and moved his head from side to side.

"I know, I know!" shouted Louisa. "S stands for snake. It makes a *sss-sss* sound and it wriggles. I won't forget S again.

"Here is another letter I can't remember. Please act it out." It was the letter I. Father stood in the middle of the room. He held himself as stiff as a poker, and puffed out his cheeks and stuck out his chest in a most important way.

"*I* am Mr. Know-it-all," he began. "*I* want attention. *I* have my way. *I* rule the——"

"I know, I know, now," sang Louisa. "The stiff letter that doesn't bend any place is 'I'."

"Do some more, please, Father," begged Anna. "You look so funny."

So Father was busy for a while and Louisa learned a lot of new letters that night. She made him do Y over and over. He stood on his head and spread his legs apart for Y. Z was the funniest letter of all. Father zigzagged across the room. He pretended to zoom about like a bee, buzzing in Baby's ear, *buzz-zz-zz*ing around Mother's geranium plants in the window. He bent himself at the knees and the hips till he was shaped like a Z. By that time, he was worn out.

"I like letters now," said Louisa. "I can hardly wait for tomorrow's lesson. If I forget at school, will you act out some of them again?" she asked hopefully.

"You won't forget them from now on." He smiled. Father was not sure that this plan would work so well in a schoolroom. It was just a little too much fun for everybody but the teacher.

V

LOUISA NEARLY DROWNS

LOUISA sat in the schoolroom and wished that she were outdoors. She could see the new green leaves on the trees on the Common, and hear the frogs croaking at the pond. It was hard to sit still, but Father didn't allow any noise at all when the other children were studying.

Father must have guessed what Louisa wanted, for he wrote her a note and laid it on her slate. It said: "Does Louisa want to play? Then tiptoe softly to the door. Play hard for a while. Then come back."

"What a nice man my father is," Louisa said to herself. No one noticed when she stole out of the door. Away she flew to the Common.

The Common made a beautiful place to play. There were walks and paths all through it. There was a pond near the middle of it, but children knew better than to wade or swim in the pond. It was swampy and full of weeds. There was no bottom to it. It was just deep, deep, oozy mud. It was called the Frog Pond.

Louisa knew how dangerous this place was, but she liked to play near it and listen to the frogs. This morning she skipped along the edge of it. She was thinking, "How fine it is to be running about in the park." Suddenly she slipped.

Her feet flew out from under her.

She had not noticed how near the edge she was. Her feet flew out from under her. Before she could cry out or grab hold of anything, she was in the water.

She felt the weeds pull her down. The mud sucked at her feet. The black water closed over her head. She knew her father couldn't come to her. Mother was home with the baby. No one would ever know what had become of her. She was drowning. She wished she had been kind to Anna, who loved her so. She wished she had not worried her mother. She struggled for breath.

Just then two strong arms reached under her. The next thing she knew she was on the bank. She looked up into the smiling face of a young colored boy. He had seen Louisa fall in. Without taking a thought for his own life he had jumped in after her. Other people had seen, too. They ran to the pond. They saw the colored boy pull her out. They carried Louisa home.

Mother hugged her and kissed her muddy little face.

Father had seen people running. He hurried home from the school.

"What has happened?" he cried.

"Louisa fell into the Frog Pond," everybody explained. "She would have drowned, without a doubt, but a colored boy saved her. He pulled her out. It is a miracle that he found her."

"Where is he?" asked Father.

No one knew.

"What's his name? Who was he?" he asked.

No one knew. Mr. Alcott asked everywhere. He wanted to thank the boy who had saved his daughter's life. He never found him. But he never forgot him. Louisa never forgot, either.

VI

LOUISA RUNS AWAY FOR THE LAST TIME

WHEN Louisa was nearly six, she noticed that things were different at home.

Mother began to do all the housework. The cook left. The maid left. Mother cooked and ironed and cleaned and sewed.

Louisa began to ask questions. She followed Mother about. "Why do you work so hard?" she asked. "Why don't you put on your pretty dress and walk with us in the park any more? Why don't we have tea parties in front of the fire?"

"I don't believe you can understand, Louisa, but I shall try to explain it to you. People are having hard times. They can't pay your father for teaching their children the way they used to. They haven't any money."

"Why don't they work and get money?

They're bad people not to pay. Father works hard."

"Hush, Louisa. They can't find work. There isn't any work. It isn't anyone's fault."

Louisa was not satisfied. She kept on asking questions. Mother was tired. Louisa's questions bothered her. "Go get your hoop and run and play," she said.

This was what Louisa wanted. She loved to roll an iron hoop from a barrel and push it along with a stick. She ran beside the hoop to guide it and keep it going as long as she could. It was great fun and hard to do. The streets were full

Not a boy could keep up with Louisa.

of boys with hoops, but not a boy could keep up with Louisa.

Other mothers didn't let their little girls play on the Common. Girls were supposed to play in the house with dolls, or they learned to embroider and sew. Louisa didn't want to be bothered with dolls. She wanted to be outdoors running and jumping and rolling hoops and playing ball.

The harder Mother worked the oftener Louisa skipped out to play. Rain or shine, hot or cold, Louisa was ready for a romp in the park. She made friends with everybody. All the children knew her. It made no difference to her whether they were rich or poor, dirty or clean, little or big, just so they let her play with them.

Often Louisa had such a good time that she forgot to come home for lunch. Mother worried when she stayed out too long. She didn't have time to look for her. Father had to go after her when he came home. Sometimes she followed the other children far from home. Father always found her. But Mother scolded Louisa.

"It is naughty of you to run away," she said.

"I don't mean to run away," said Louisa. "I just forget."

Times grew harder. The Alcotts had to move into a smaller house in a different neighborhood.

One day Louisa followed her new friends to the city dump, a place to which people carried their ashes and trash. It was the first time she had seen this place. She thought it was wonderful. She found all kinds of funny things to look at. Lunchtime came before she knew it. The other children said, "Eat with us. We have plenty." They built a fire out on the dump and baked potatoes in the ashes. They had hard, stale bread. They shared with Louisa. She thought she had never tasted such good food.

Louisa began to get tired. She wanted to go

home and tell her mother about the new playground she had found. She wanted her to know her new friends. But Louisa couldn't find the way home.

She was not frightened. "Father will soon find me," she said to herself. "He always does." The other children left. It began to grow cold. Louisa started to walk along the street.

"If I walk far enough, I shall come to my home," she thought. She walked until she was too tired to go farther. It was growing dark. She saw a lamplighter far down the street. She ran to meet him as he moved along with his short ladder on his back. At every post he would set up his ladder, climb up and light the gas lamp.

Louisa loved to watch for the lamplighter from a window of her house and wave to him as he went by.

"He will show me the way home," she said to herself now. But this was not the lamplighter that she knew. He had no idea where she lived, and went on down the street. Louisa was alone again. She was tired and cold and hungry.

A big, shaggy-haired dog came and stood beside her. He licked her face. She put her arms around his neck. He felt nice and warm. He lay down beside her. Louisa rested her head on the dog. He made a nice pillow. "I'll wait here for Papa," she decided. Soon she fell fast asleep.

She woke up suddenly. It was dark. She couldn't remember where she was. A bell was ringing near by. A man was calling something over and over in a loud voice. "Lost, lost. A little girl, six years old, in a pink frock, white hat and new green shoes."

"Why, that's me," she cried and ran to the man. It was not her father. It was the town crier. He had been sent to find her. Father and Mother had looked for her all afternoon. When it began to grow dark, they were greatly worried.

It was the town crier.

So they went to the town crier. He was a man
with a good strong voice. He carried a bell with
him. He would go through the streets ringing
the bell and crying out the news. When people

heard the bell, they ran to their doors and windows to hear what he had to say.

Father told the crier how Louisa was dressed, how old she was, and where she lived. The crier started out at once with his bell.

When he found Louisa, he did not take her home at once. He said, "It is a long way to your house. You will be too tired to walk there until you've had something to eat. My home is near. I'll take you to my wife. She'll give you some supper. Then I'll take you home."

The town crier's wife was kind to Louisa. She gave her molasses and bread on a pretty tin plate. The plate had the letters of the alphabet around the edge. The crier's wife was surprised that Louisa could read them easily.

"Oh, I could read a long time ago," said Louisa. "My father taught me when I was little." The wife thought Louisa was still pretty little.

When Louisa started home, she wanted to take the dog with her. "He likes me," she said. "See how he looks at me and how he wags his tail. I'll take him with me."

"No, no. He belongs to a boy who lives near," said the crier.

"I want him anyway," said Louisa. "He'll feel sad if I leave him behind. Ask the little boy if I can have him. See, he won't stay behind."

"We must get started," said the crier. "Your poor mother will be sick with worry."

Louisa began to cry. "I want the dog," she sobbed.

"What's this?" spoke up the wife. "What a sight! A big girl who can read and write crying like a baby!"

That hushed Louisa right away. She stopped crying, and patted the dog good-by. She thanked the woman for her supper, and went off with the crier.

What a thankful mother took a tired little Louisa into her arms that night! How Father shook the crier's hand! Anna came running downstairs in her nightcap and gown. Lizzie woke up and pattered down the steps. "Come, tell me," she called.

After they were all safe in bed, Louisa told Anna and Lizzie about the dump and the baked potatoes and the tin plate and the friendly dog.

"Tomorrow," said Lizzie, after Louisa had told them everything, "I'll go to the dump, too, with Weezie. We'll both get lost."

"No, no," said Anna. "Poor mother has been too worried. She cried and cried when she couldn't find you, Louisa."

That made Louisa cry, too.

But she felt important the next morning; everyone made such a fuss over her. That didn't last long, though. Mother decided that she needed to learn a lesson. It was high time that she remembered to stay nearer home. "There'll be no more running away," she said.

She took Louisa to the front room where everybody who looked in the door would see her. She tied one end of a piece of string to Louisa's wrist. She tied the other end to the arms of the sofa. All day she left her there. She even brought her lunch to her there. Everybody stared at Louisa. Mother said, "Louisa runs away just as our kitten does, so we have to tie her up."

Louisa had plenty of time to think that over. She decided she wanted to be treated like Mother's little girl and not like a pet animal. Late in the afternoon, when no one was near, she called out:

"I'm sorry I worried you, Mother. I surely will never forget again. Do you think you can love me a little?"

Then Mother took Louisa in her arms and

kisssed her and hugged her tight. "Of course, I love my dear little runaway," she said. "I'm sure we'll never have to do this again." They didn't, either.

VII

THE ALCOTTS SHARE THEIR BREAKFAST

PEOPLE everywhere were poor the winter that
Louisa was seven. There was very little
money and almost no work. Mr. Alcott was paid
less and less for teaching, so the Alcotts had less
and less food on the table. They had enough to
eat, though, and they had such merry times that
at first they didn't really notice how plain the
meals were.

After a while Anna and Louisa tired of having
the same thing over and over. They missed the
good puddings and pies. That wasn't the worst
of it. There came a time when there wasn't any
sugar.

One morning Louisa threw down her spoon
and said crossly, "I'm tired of rice without any
sugar. I want a cinnamon roll and muffins."

"We used to have good things all the time,"
said Anna. "Now, we don't have anything but
rice and more rice and more rice, and sometimes
dry bread."

"Rice is a good wholesome food," said Mother
cheerfully. "It is better for you without sugar."

The two little girls didn't answer. They just
sat there and wouldn't eat.

Then Father said, "There are little children
near us who will be glad to have your breakfast.
These are dreadful times. People are starving
all around here." He rose from the table.
"Come with me," he said. "Bring your bowls of
rice with you."

Father went out of the house. Anna followed
him carrying her bowl, and Louisa followed
Anna. People turned to stare at the strange
parade. Father led the girls down the street to a
neat little house. He knocked. A thin, bent
woman answered the door. When she saw who

Father led the girls down the street to a neat little house.

was there, and when she saw the steaming bowls, she cried out, "God bless you, Mr. Alcott." Then she called, "Come, boys, come. Here is Mr. Alcott and his daughters with food."

Two pale little boys ran to the door. Their eyes opened wide when they saw what Anna and Louisa carried. The girls handed them each a bowl and watched them gulp down the food. The boys were so grateful that Anna and Louisa were sorry they hadn't brought last night's supper, too.

"We shall come again soon," they promised. "We shall bring you our share of the pudding on Sunday. Mother makes the best pudding in the world."

On the way home Louisa asked, "Is their father out of work? Is that why they were so hungry?"

"No, it is worse than that, little Louisa. Their father has work, but he drinks. When he is drunk, he forgets about his little boys. Often there is no wood in the house, either."

"Then, Father," said Louisa stoutly, "each day you must tell us if they have food. I shall give one of my meals to those poor children."

"So shall I," said Anna. "We'll share one meal each day with somebody who is hungry."

"That's the way I like to hear my little girls

talk," said Father. "Mother will be proud of you."

Many and many a day after that people saw the Alcotts carrying food to the hungry.

VIII

MORE CHANGES

"WE SHALL have school here at home to-day," said Father one morning.

"Why, what will the children at the school do?" asked Anna.

"There isn't any school," said Father sadly.

"Is the beautiful school gone?" He nodded. Louisa began to cry. "Where are your books, and the pictures, and your fine desk?"

"They are gone just while times are bad," Father assured her. "It costs a great deal of money to have a school like that. In the mean-time, I'll teach you each morning before I leave to go to work. This morning Mother and I have a surprise for you." He brought out two little books. He gave one to each of them.

"Why, there isn't any writing in mine," said Louisa.

"Nor in mine," chimed in Anna.

"You are to do the writing yourselves, he said. "You must write in your books each day."

"What shall I write?" asked Louisa.

"Write about the things you want to remember. Write your thoughts. Write about anything that troubles you. It will help you clear your mind to write down what you worry about. Put in the book the everyday happenings here at home. These are to be your diaries. I want you to keep them all your lives."

That is how Louisa started her first book.

The school did not open again. Anna and Louisa learned their lessons at home. They didn't go to any other school. Besides the lessons they learned in books, they learned to sweep and dust and cook and sew.

Anna loved to help keep house. She was quick to learn. Louisa didn't like housework. She hated to dust and sew.

"I should have been a boy," she said. "I wasn't meant to be a girl. I like to climb trees and jump fences and run like the wind."

More and more often she slipped out of the house and left her share of the work to Anna. Anna didn't mind. When Louisa came home, she always had exciting adventures to tell. She whispered them each night to Anna.

IX

AN ADVENTURE THAT HAD A BAD ENDING

ONE day Louisa didn't come home.

"I am afraid something has happened to her," Mother said to Father when he returned from work. "I am sure she has not run away. I have called and called. She does not answer."

Father started on the run for the water front.

The Alcotts had moved again. This time they lived close to the ocean. They could look out and see the boats and the shipping at the docks. Louisa loved to play on the docks where she could see all that was going on.

There was a piano factory close by. At the side of the factory was a long, sloping runway. It was used to wheel pianos down to the dock where they were loaded into ships or into moving vans. At the top of the runway were big wooden packing cases in which they shipped the pianos.

Louisa liked to run up and down the runway. This particular day she saw some boys get into one of the packing cases and go rolling down the runway in it. The big box rolled faster and faster down the slope and ended in a great crash at the bottom.

"Oh, they must all be killed," thought Louisa in a fright. But the boys weren't hurt at all.

"It's fun," they shouted. "It makes a terrible noise when it hits the bottom, but you just hold on tight. It shakes you up a little, that's all. Of course, no girl would dare do it," they added. They said that to tease Louisa.

Louisa immediately ran up and tried to start one of the cases down by herself.

"Wait, wait," cried Will, one of the older boys. "Don't try it. We were only teasing."

She saw some boys get

into one of the packing cases.

"You did it. I can do it," said Louisa stubbornly.

"Someone must go with you to push it and get it started straight. If you are not careful, you will roll off the edge and be killed."

"Then come here and start it," said Louisa impatiently.

"I don't think your mother would like it," Will said honestly.

"Hurry up," insisted Louisa. "Don't be a sissy." She stepped into the packing case. He gave it a push and jumped in, too.

How it roared and rumbled inside the case! What a tremendous crash it made at the bottom! Louisa loved it.

"Let's do it again," she begged. So they did it again, and again and again, until it was tame sport.

"Let's try rolling down in a barrel," said Louisa. "That would be much faster."

"Yes, and much more dangerous," said Will. "You couldn't jump out and stop yourself if you went too close to the edge. I won't let you do it."

"Let her try it," said another boy, who had a mean, sly look. He rolled a barrel to the top of the runway for Louisa. She got into it.

"Please don't do it," begged Will.

But the second boy said, "You keep out of this. Just because you're a 'fraid-cat doesn't make her one."

That decided Louisa. She was flattered by his words. "Give me a push," she called from inside the barrel.

The mean boy gave the barrel a nudge with his foot. He didn't take care to start it straight at all. The barrel rolled toward the edge of the runway. Will shouted. He sprang after it, tried to stop it, but barely touched it. Faster and faster it rolled toward the edge. It seemed fairly to fly through the air, and then it *was* flying through the air. Halfway down it bounded off the runway, crashed to the ground below and broke into pieces.

The boys couldn't bear to look to see what had happened to Louisa. There was no sound from under the wreck. Some of them crawled down to it. Will was sobbing, "She was such a jolly little girl. I shouldn't have let her do it. I'm older. I knew better."

Louisa lay still and white.

The mean boy said, "Oh, she ain't hurt."

"If she is, I'll give you the thrashing of your life," said the other. The mean boy ran away.

By this time the rest of the boys had reached the barrel. They lifted off the broken pieces. Louisa lay under them, still and white.

All the boys ran away then, but Will. He called after them to go for her father. But they were badly frightened. They made off and hid. "We'll all be put in jail," they thought, "because we let her go down in the barrel and get hurt."

Will was afraid to lift Louisa. He feared he would hurt her. He didn't want to leave her, either. So he just sat there and called and called for help.

Father heard him and came running. The boy told him all that had happened. Father leaned over Louisa. "She's alive," he said, "but I can't tell how badly she's hurt."

Will helped Father drag a wide board to

where Louisa lay. Father lifted her onto it. He sent Will for help. Men came quickly. One ran for a doctor, another to warn Mrs. Alcott, and others helped carry Louisa home. When they laid her inside the house, she opened her eyes and was astonished to see everybody gathered about her. She looked at the doctor.

"Who's hurt? What's the matter?" she asked, and sat up. Then everyone else was astonished.

The doctor looked Louisa over carefully. She was hardly hurt at all. The wind had been knocked out of her and there was a bump on her head. But the next day she was as good as new.

X

LOUISA GETS A REWARD

ONE evening after Anna and Louisa had gone to bed, Mother and Father had a talk.

"Louisa is growing into a regular tomboy," said Mother. "She plays in the streets day in and day out."

"She doesn't run away any more," said Father.

"No, but she wants to be outdoors all the time. She loses her temper more and more easily. The children in this neighborhood play too roughly. The boys tease her and put her up to all kinds of pranks. I wish she would play quietly at home with Anna and her little friends. They have such good times with their dolls."

"That's too tame for our Louisa," said Father, "but it isn't right for the boys to tease her. Perhaps we'd better give her a vacation."

"I'll let her visit our friends the Carletons in Providence. They have often begged me to send them one of my girls for a while. The change will do Louisa good."

"We'll let her go as a reward for not running away," said Father.

A few days after this talk, Mother asked Louisa, "How would you like to go on a trip?"

"You mean go clear away in a stagecoach?"

"How soon do I start?" asked Louisa. She ran about the house, upstairs and down, gathering her belongings together. She thought she was leaving in a few minutes.

"Oh, you have plenty of time," said Mother. "You can't leave until Saturday. Anna, do you think you and I can manage the house by ourselves?"

Anna wanted to go on the trip, too, but she was proud that Mother counted on her help.

"I'll take all the care of Lizzie," she said sweetly.

Lizzie had been listening. Now she ran and hugged Anna about the knees so tight that Anna fell down. Louisa tripped over Anna. Lizzie saw them both on the floor, so she fell down on Louisa. Father came in at that moment. He saw the children on the floor, so he said, "What kind of a game is this?" Then he pretended to stumble and fall down, too.

Mother laughed to see her family in such high spirits. Then everybody jumped up and helped Mother get the supper on the table. They were all so happy making plans for Louisa's vacation that nobody noticed how skimpy the evening meal was. The boiled rice smelled and tasted unusually good. They scraped the kettle clean.

XI

LOUISA GOES ON A JOURNEY

Louisa was awake long before daylight Saturday morning. She listened for Mother, but didn't hear her. "I wonder if Mother has overslept. Perhaps she has forgotten that this is the day I leave."

Louisa got up and dressed. Mother had packed most of her things the night before. Louisa put her nightgown and hairbrush and bedroom slippers in her trunk and closed it. It was a little too heavy for her to carry, so she dragged it down the stairs *thump, thump, thump*. She pulled it across the living room and set it outside the front door. Then she put on her coat and hat and sat down on the doorstep to wait.

"*I'm* not going to be late," Louisa said to herself.

Mother came downstairs a little later. "I'll make muffins this morning," she said to herself. "Louisa is fond of them and I'll have them as a going-away surprise."

Father and Lizzie came to the table when Mother called out that breakfast was ready. "Where's Louisa?" she asked.

"She was already gone when I got up," said Anna.

"Why, I haven't seen her," said Mother anxiously. "Surely Louisa hasn't run away this morning, of all mornings."

Father called loudly. There was no answer. "I'll take a look up and down the street. Louisa may have gone to tell her friends good-by," he said.

He opened the front door. There was little Louisa, leaning against her trunk, sound asleep.

Father carried her in to the breakfast table. Louisa was astounded when she opened her eyes.

There was Louisa sound asleep.

She had been dreaming. She thought she had
gone to Providence and come back again already. But when she smelled the muffins, she sat
up, wide awake. She was as hungry as if she
really had been on a journey. Mother filled a
lunch basket for her. She knew Louisa would be
hungry before she reached the end of her trip.

Louisa might have gone to Providence by
train, but it cost more than by stagecoach. She
had always wanted to ride in a coach. Now at
last she was going to have her wish. The coaches

were pulled by four fine big horses. The driver
sat on a high seat in front. He carried a great
long whip which he cracked in the air above the
horses' heads.

Mother and Father and Anna and Elizabeth
went with Louisa to the street crossing where the
coach passed. When they saw it coming, they all
began to wave. Father waved his hat. Mother
and the girls waved their handkerchiefs.

For a moment Louisa thought the big horses
were going to thunder by, but the driver pulled
on the reins and shouted, "Whoa!" in a tremendous voice. The coach stopped beside them.

Father spoke to the driver. He told him where
Louisa was going to stay in Providence. The
driver said, "I know the Carletons. I'll see that
your little girl gets there safely."

Father was glad. He paid the driver and lifted
Louisa into the coach. Then the driver cracked
his whip and away they went.

Mother and Anna and Lizzie waved as long as the coach was in sight. Anna and Lizzie cried on the way back. "It's no fun at home without Louisa," they said.

Louisa didn't cry. She looked all around the inside of the coach. It wasn't so fine as she had expected. She had thought the seats would be covered with red velvet the way they were in the story books. They weren't. They were covered with black leather. The leather was old and torn.

She couldn't see anything but the sky out of the window, the seat was so low. But it was exciting to feel the coach sway from side to side.

"We must be going very fast."

Louisa counted the people in the coach, talked to each one, and asked where they were going and how long they were going to stay.

"How long will it take to get to Providence?" she asked a man across from her. "Are we nearly there?"

He laughed. "We've just started," he said.

"When can I get a drink?"

"The driver will stop to rest the horses at Woonsocket. You can get a drink there."

"How soon will we get to Woonsocket?"

"Pretty soon," the man replied patiently.

An old woman sat next to Louisa. She held a basket on her knees.

"What's in your basket?" asked Louisa.

The old woman said, "Little girls should be seen and not heard."

"What does she mean by that?" Louisa asked her friend across the aisle.

"She thinks the little girl sitting next to her is talking too much," smiled the man.

Louisa didn't like that. She frowned and stuck out her lower lip. She said to herself, "I don't like this old lady. I hope she drops her basket. I hope it breaks open and spills everything in it all over every place."

Louisa didn't say anything more for a long time. She sulked and looked down her nose. Her little face that had been so bright and sunny looked like a thundercloud.

The coach rumbled along. Sometimes the road was rough and the coach would jolt and bump. Sometimes it was dark inside. Louisa could see branches of trees and thick foliage out the window. She knew they were going through forests. Pretty soon they went up a hill; Louisa could tell by the way the coach tipped endways. The tops of the trees went down below the window sill. Then the trees came up again and the coach tipped up the other end. They were going down the other side of the hill. Louisa could not stay on the seat. She kept sliding off.

The old lady next to her did not notice. She was asleep. Louisa picked herself up off the floor a third time. The basket on the old lady's knees slipped and fell, too. Louisa lifted it. It was not very heavy. It wobbled in a funny way. "There must be something alive in it," she guessed. She put it back on the seat. The coach gave a great lurch. The basket fell with a thump. The catch on the lid broke. Out tumbled a beautiful big cat. Louisa let out a squeal of delight. She stooped to pick up the cat. She loved cats. But the cat gave a great leap. It sprang out the window, right over Louisa's head. Louisa screamed. The old lady awoke.

"Oh, oh, oh!" she cried. "My beautiful cat. My lovely cat. Where is it?"

"It jumped out the window," cried Louisa.

"It will be killed!" cried the lady. "Stop the coach!"

Louisa banged on the window under the driver's seat.

"Stop! Stop!"

The driver heard the screams. He shouted "Whoa! Whoa!" to the horses. He pulled on the reins so hard that the horses stood on their hind legs. "The door must have come un-latched," he thought. "The little girl must have fallen out." He jumped down from his place. He ran to the side of the coach and looked in.

"What's the matter?" he panted.

"The old lady's cat!" cried Louisa. "It jumped out of the window. Open the door! I'll go back and get it for her."

"I'll do nothing of the kind," shouted the driver. "Hold up the coach for a cat? I guess not!" He was angry. "I've never been late get-ting into Woonsocket before. I don't intend to spoil my record for a silly cat."

The old lady was crying.

As quick as a cat herself, Louisa climbed to the window ledge. She jumped out onto the driver's shoulders. "Yes, you will wait," she cried. "Don't you see the old lady is crying?" She boxed the driver's ears. She pulled his hair.

He was dumfounded. He held her with one hand and scratched his head with the other. Then he laughed and laughed. He set Louisa down on the ground. "Run along after the cat," he said. "I'll wait a few minutes. But mind you don't chase it into the woods. You'll get lost."

The old lady called after Louisa. "I'd better come with you. The cat won't come to you.

She talked to the cat softly.

He's frightened. He never would go to strangers." She scrambled down from the coach.

"Don't worry," Louisa called back. "All animals like me."

Soon she saw the cat hiding in the brush at the side of the road. It crawled farther back toward the woods when she came near. She talked to it softly, then walked right up to it and picked it up. The woman could scarcely believe her eyes. "He never did that before," she murmured.

They went back and the driver mended the old lady's basket. She fastened the cat in firmly. She climbed into the coach. The driver lifted Louisa up to the step.

"How would you like to ride up in front with me?" he asked.

"Oh, I'd love to!" she answered. The driver swung her up onto the high seat.

XII

HORSES ARE LIKE PEOPLE

LOUISA wished Anna and Lizzie could see her. She wished the boys who teased her could see her too. She was so high she could touch the branches of the trees and look down into the birds' nests. She stood up on the seat and stretched her arms.

"It feels just like flying," she cried.

The driver pulled her down onto the seat. "You'll have to sit still and hold tight," he said. "You might get dizzy and fall off."

Louisa didn't get dizzy, for she loved to stand on high places. She sat down, though, because the driver was worried.

"What are the horses' names?" she asked.

The driver grinned. He liked to talk about his horses. "That one up in front on this side is

"It feels just like flying," she cried.

Bess," he said. "She's a good puller. She always does more than her share."

"My little sister is named Bess. Only we call her Lizzie."

"The horse next to Bess is Jim. The two back horses are Mars and Bill."

"Do Mars and Bill go in front sometimes?"

"I used to change them around but they work better behind Bess."

"Do you always put Jim next to Bess?"

"I changed Jim around too when I first got him. I nearly sold him one day. He didn't seem to get along with the others. I tried him with Bill. He kicked and bit at Bill. Then I tried him with Mars. He wouldn't work at all with Mars. He just loafed and let Mars do all the pulling. I was disgusted with him. Then, one day, I put him up front with Bess. They got along fine together. Jim worked as hard as Bess. Now he is one of the best horses I ever had. He and Bess understand each other."

"I guess horses are like people," said Louisa.

"You're exactly right," agreed the driver.

There were so many things Louisa wanted to know that the time passed quickly. The driver was surprised when they came to the first houses of Woonsocket. The horses began to run.

"We've made a quick trip," the driver said. "Do you see the inn up ahead?"

Louisa saw a white stone building with a sign hanging out in front.

"That's where we stop to change horses. This team's getting tired. They know they get to eat here, and rest. That's why they're hurrying."

The horses fairly flew. The driver cracked his whip in the air with a flourish. People ran to the doors to watch the stagecoach pass. Louisa waved and shouted. They whirled up to the inn in a cloud of dust.

The driver pulled the horses to a stop. The innkeeper came out. He invited the passengers to eat and rest. The stableboys ran out and un-hitched the tired horses and led them into the barn at the side of the inn. Then they brought out four new horses and backed them up to the coach.

The driver lifted Louisa down. "You can buy your lunch in the inn," he said.

"Mother packed some lunch in a box for me."

"Then you can sit out here and watch them hitch up the fresh horses, if you like."

Louisa liked that. She got a cold drink from a well in front of the inn.

Soon the people began to come out and get into the coach again. The driver set Louisa inside this time. He thought she might take a nap.

Later in the afternoon he stopped the horses at the top of a long hill. They were breathing so hard their sides went in and out like a bellows. He let them rest awhile, and went around to the door of the coach to see how his little passenger was getting along. She was sitting as still as a mouse. The big cat was on her lap.

"I want to ride outside in the fresh air, please," she said, and put the cat back in his basket.

The driver lifted Louisa onto the front seat

again. Before they had gone far she knew the names of these horses, too.

It didn't seem long before the afternoon had passed and they came to Providence. The coach rumbled over the cobblestone streets and pulled up at a large inn, crowded with people. "We can never find Mother's friend and her husband among all these strangers," Louisa thought.

The driver looked down at the many heads from his high place. Suddenly he touched his cap with his whip. "There they are!" he said, pointing over the crowd. He took Louisa to them. "Here's a little bundle I've brought you from Boston," he said. "I told Mr. Alcott I would see that it arrived safe in your hands."

Mrs. Carleton took Louisa into her arms. "I would know this little girl anywhere!" she cried. "She looks just like her mother."

The driver brought Louisa's trunk. Louisa thanked him for taking such good care of her.

He patted her on the head and said, "We'll have another ride together when it's time for you to go home again."

The old lady leaned out of the coach and thanked Louisa again and again for saving her cat.

Everybody waved good-by, then Louisa went home with Mr. and Mrs. Carleton.

Everybody waved good-by.

XIII

A BED FOR A FAIRY QUEEN

LOUISA called the Carletons Auntie and Uncle, though they weren't really related to her.

Auntie's house was tall and narrow. It didn't have a front porch. Stone steps led to the front door. Inside was a wide hallway. On one side of the hall was the door to the dining room. On the other side were the doors to the big double parlor and the library.

A wide straight stairway led upstairs from the front door.

When Auntie and Uncle and Louisa entered the front door, a tall boy came running down the stairs to meet them. He was Christopher, Auntie's son. Louisa liked him at once. He shook hands with her as if she were a young lady.

"I'll take your bag upstairs for you," he said. "Would you like to come up?. I'll show you where your room is." Louisa followed him up the wide steps. On the second floor was another hall with more steps going up from it. "Those stairs go to the third story," said Christopher. "The maid and the cook have their rooms up there. Above that is the attic. I'll take you up some day. You can see all over the city from there."

He led the way to a door at the front of the house. "This is to be your room," he said.

"You mean a room all my very own?" It seemed strange to Louisa to have a room by herself.

"Of course," replied Christopher. "Mother has had lots of fun getting it ready for you." He threw the door open.

Louisa was so astonished that she could only stand and stare. In front of her was a great four-poster bed. It was covered with light blue silk that hung from the ceiling to the floor. The bedspread was blue, too, and trimmed with lace ruffles. It looked like a fairy queen's bed.

It looked like a fairy queen's bed.

She looked all around the room with wide eyes. She had never seen anything so lovely. It was all like fairyland to her. On one side of the room was a white marble fireplace. It had shining brass andirons. A bright little copper kettle hung by a crane over the coals in the fire-place. On each end of the mantel were brass candlesticks with pretty crystals dangling from them. There was a china clock in the middle of the mantel. On one side of it a little china boy bowed to a pretty china girl who stood on the other side.

On a small gold table near her bed was a lamp. The bottom of it was china with pink roses and little blue flowers painted on it. The top half was clear glass. In one corner of the room was a dressing table with a mirror in a gold frame above it. The floor was covered with a thick flowered carpet.

There were so many pretty things to look at that Louisa thought she never could see them all. Auntie came up to help her unpack. She was glad that Louisa was so happy about her room.

A tinkling bell sounded from downstairs. "That's the dinner bell," said Auntie. "We'll finish unpacking tomorrow. Come along. You must be hungry."

But Louisa was too tired to eat. Almost before she could see what was on her plate, she was asleep.

"Poor little darling," said Auntie.

Uncle gathered her up in his arms and carried her upstairs. She didn't even wake up when Auntie got her ready for bed and tucked her in. Auntie smiled at the rosy little face. She kissed Louisa, then blew out the lamp and went back downstairs.

XIV

NEW FACES AND NEW WAYS

LOUISA was awakened by a crackling sound. At first she thought, "That's Father starting the morning fire. It's time to get up." She opened her eyes, then laughed aloud.

The noise she had heard was the fire in her pretty white fireplace. The maid was laying fresh kindling on it. She turned around when she heard Louisa laugh. "So you are awake already?"

"Who are you?" asked Louisa.

"I am Ellen. There's warm water for you in the pitcher. I'll put the tub in front of the fire and place the screen behind it. That will give you a nice, warm place to bathe. It is still chilly in the mornings."

Louisa thought it was funny to go to so much trouble just to wash, but she didn't say anything.

Ellen was going to help her dress, too. Louisa had to laugh at that.

"I always dress myself," she said. "Even little Lizzie can dress herself. Anna and I help her sometimes. Mother has too many other things to do. She hasn't time to help big girls like Anna and me."

Ellen was glad Louisa could take care of herself. She had much to do. "Breakfast will be ready soon," she said. "You'll hear the bell."

Louisa had always been called to breakfast by Mother's cheery voice. She wondered if Mother were calling Anna and Lizzie and Father now.

Just then the bell rang. Louisa ran to the stairs. She started down, and saw the smooth banister. "What a wonderful slide it would make!" she thought. In a moment she was astride it. Down she flew. This was the smooth-est railing she had ever been on. She came to the

Down she flew!

end but was going too fast to stop and landed on
the floor with a thump.

Ellen heard her fall and came running.
"What happened?" she gasped.

"I slid off the banister."

"Tch, tch, tch," clucked Ellen. "Nice little girls don't slide down banisters. Only tomboys do that. We don't like tomboys in Providence. Come to breakfast now. The others are waiting."

Louisa ran into the dining room. "Good morning, every——" What she saw on the breakfast table made her stop short. She had never seen so much food at one time. She was used to cereal and nothing more. Here on the table were bacon and eggs, biscuits, marmalade, tea, cocoa, milk, and cereal, also.

Ellen served her bacon and eggs. Louisa didn't know what to do. There was something that Auntie had forgotten. The Alcotts were vegetarians. Vegetarians don't eat meat. Louisa had been taught to eat what was set before her, but she couldn't eat the bacon. So she just looked at Auntie. When Auntie saw Louisa looking at her, she remembered.

"Louisa doesn't eat meat, Ellen. Her people are vegetarians, so, while she is here, serve her fruits and vegetables and plenty of bread and milk, but no meat."

Ellen had never heard of vegetarians before. She thought the Alcotts must be queer people. She told Cook about it. Cook wanted to see a child who had never eaten meat. "She must be awful skinny and pale," she thought. She came from the kitchen and peeked through the pantry door at Louisa. She saw a rosy-cheeked, curly-haired, bright-eyed little girl at the table. She was astonished, and shook her head in wonder.

After breakfast Louisa went into the big front parlor. A desk with shelves of books above it stood in one corner. On the desk was a beautiful red quill pen. Louisa could hardly wait to take hold of it.

All morning she thought about the red quill

pen. Finally she said, "I think I'd better write a letter to Mother."

Auntie didn't know that Louisa could really write, but she said, "I know your mother will be glad to hear that you are all right. You may use the red quill, if you like."

That, of course, was what Louisa wanted. She sat down to write, but the chair was too low for her. She climbed onto the desk to reach books on the shelves so that she could put a few fat ones in the chair. She had her arms full and was about to jump down, when she tripped on the inkwell. Over she went. Down went the books and Louisa, knocking the quill off the desk and spilling ink everywhere.

Auntie heard her fall. So did Ellen and Christopher. All came running. They heard Louisa crying. "Oh dear," thought Auntie, "she's hurt and her visit's just begun." They picked her up.

"It's the quill that's hurt, not me," she explained. Ellen didn't say anything, but she looked hard at all the muss she would have to clean up.

Louisa said, "Let me help you wipe up the ink, Ellen."

"The quill's easily mended," said Christopher. He took out his pocket knife and sharpened the quill point so that it was as good as new. Then he put a big dictionary on the chair, and Louisa started to write her letter.

She began: "Dear Mother, I——" and then the bell rang. Luncheon was ready.

It seemed to Louisa that all she did was eat.

"I wish I could send some of my dessert to Lizzie and Anna," she thought. She fairly stuffed herself to bursting with cake and custard. Funny little Louisa wanted to eat enough at one time to last all summer.

XV

A FUNERAL PARTY

L UNCHEON was over. Louisa saw several little girls come down the street carrying dolls. She watched them. "Oh dear! They're turning in here!" She ran to Auntie.

"Are those girls coming to see me? I don't want to play dolls."

"It will be rude of you not to play. They are trying to be friendly."

Louisa frowned. "I'll play dolls with them just this one time. Then they'll have to play my way. I won't tell them I haven't a doll. They can think mine's broken."

Auntie let the little callers in and introduced them to Louisa. As soon as Auntie had gone upstairs, they began to play "grownups" with their dolls.

"How's your little girl this afternoon?" they asked.

"Oh, I am brokenhearted about her. My child was killed just before I left home," replied Louisa.

"How dreadful!" they cried. "What happened?"

"She fell out of a tree. She was such a tomboy, always climbing trees, no matter how I scolded. Yesterday she fell asleep in the treetop. I heard the birds making a fuss, and ran out. There lay Dolly on the ground."

"Dear, dear! Did you have a funeral?"

Louisa hadn't thought of that. "We're having the funeral today," she said quickly. "Will you help me bury her?"

"Yes, indeed we will," they said eagerly. "First we must hurry home and put on funeral clothes."

"Maybe Auntie has some that will do. She has an attic."

Auntie said of course she had dress-up things. She sent Ellen up with the children to open the trunks.

"You can play there all afternoon, if you like," she said.

The girls squealed with delight when they saw what was in the trunks.

"Oh, ooh, oo-ooh! What an elegant funeral we shall have," they cried.

"May I wear this black skirt, Louisa?" begged one.

"Please let me have the little bonnet."

"Oh my, my! Help me put on this corset, will you?"

"Here's a hat with a black veil that will be just right for the mother to wear. And here's a pair of high, button shoes. They're kind of big, but they will look nice under a long skirt."

The girls squealed with delight when they saw what was
in the trunk.

They were all talking at once and were so excited they forgot to act sad. But when all were dressed, they became quite sober and talked softly and were very sweet and sympathetic to Louisa.

They began to plan the funeral. Suddenly Louisa remembered she didn't have a doll to bury. She went to Auntie and whispered her trouble to her. "We can't have a funeral without somebody to bury."

Auntie thought a minute. "I have an old doll head somewhere. We can take a roll of cloth and tie it onto the head and make it look like a body. We'll cover it with lace and no one will guess the difference. You run back to the girls and make the coffin while I find the head."

Louisa and the others found a shoe box. They lined it with white satin that was in the trunk, and covered it with velvet.

"It's the finest coffin we ever had," they declared. Auntie called Louisa downstairs just as they were finishing. She handed her the doll, all fixed up. When Louisa saw it, she burst into tears.

"Why, Louisa, what is the matter? What's wrong?"

"She's just so beautiful," sobbed Louisa. "I've never seen such a sweet doll. I can't bear to think that she's dead."

Auntie tried to comfort her. "You can have her come alive again tomorrow."

"That doesn't make her alive now. We have to have the funeral, because everything is ready."

When Louisa laid the doll in the coffin, all the girls cried. They sang a sorrowful tune as they carried the coffin down the attic stairs, past the third floor, through the upstairs hall, and down the front steps. The little procession ended in the back yard near a lilac bush. There they dug a grave and lined it with grass and flowers, and buried Louisa's child. They placed a stone over the top, and were about to start crying again, when they heard Auntie calling.

They ran to the house to see what she wanted. She had a tea party waiting for them. At sight of the pretty cakes and sandwiches they forgot all about the funeral.

At sight of the pretty cakes and sandwiches they forgot all
about the funeral.

After tea they took off their fancy dresses and put them back in the trunks in the attic.

"We must go home now, Louisa. This is the best time we have had all year."

"Be sure to come tomorrow," Louisa called after them as they left, "and bring your children." She had forgotten that she didn't like dolls.

Early the next morning she ran out and dug up Auntie's doll. The night in the ground hadn't seemed to hurt it, but Louisa thought it might have taken cold, and kept it in bed with a mustard plaster for a while.

The little girls came nearly every day. Sometimes they played that their dolls were naughty children who had to be punished; or they had the measles. Other days they were princesses. There was not a dull minute. Louisa had such a good time that she almost forgot her tomboy ways. Then something happened.

XVI

THE ATTIC HOLDS A PRISONER

IT WAS a dark, rainy afternoon. Louisa's friends couldn't come over to play. She felt cross and grumpy, and went up to her pretty room and leaned on the window sill. She pressed her nose against the windowpane and made faces at the raindrops. She looked down into the street. Some ragged little children were running about in the rain. They were jumping mud puddles and having a merry time. It made her homesick to see them.

"At home I can play in the rain, too. That's lots more fun than staying in a stuffy old house. I'm tired of being a girl all the time. I'm going outdoors."

She peeked out into the hall. No one was in sight. Auntie was making calls. Ellen was on the third floor; Cook was out for the afternoon.

Louisa slid down the banisters and skipped out the front door. Soon she was jumping mud puddles and rolling hoops and having a gay time with the children in the street.

They were playing near a pastry shop. After a while they stopped and looked into the window. There were gingerbread boys fastened to pieces of cardboard, jars of peppermint candy, boxes of maple sugar, puddings and pies.

"I wish I had that gingerbread," sighed a little boy.

"I'd like to have that apple pie," said another.

"I could eat everything in the window," cried another.

A very small boy began to cry. "I'm hungry," he bawled.

Louisa looked at him. He was pale and thin. "Are you really hungry?"

"Of course he's hungry. We're all of us hungry all the time."

"Oh, how selfish I've been," cried Louisa. "I've had cake and pie and all kinds of good things at Auntie's. I forgot all about sharing. Come with me," she called to them. "There's plenty of food at Auntie's. There'll be enough for everybody."

She led them into the pantry and opened the cupboards.

Louisa ran into the house and down to the kitchen. No one was there. She looked into the pantry. No one was there. Louisa didn't want to keep the children waiting. She led them into the pantry and opened the cupboards. How fine it was that there was plenty of everything! She gave the children potatoes and rice and eggs and flour and bread and meat, and cake and pudding. They couldn't speak, they were so surprised. Louisa helped the little boy carry his load home. It took her longer than she thought.

She skipped all the way back to Auntie's house. "I am happier than I've been any day since I left Mother," she said to herself. "It's because I thought of somebody else. 'It is best to give away the nice things,' Mother said. Now I know what she meant."

She ran into Auntie's house as happy as a lark.

Auntie and Cook and Ellen were standing in

the front hall. Ellen looked cross. Cook looked angry. Auntie looked stern.

"Louisa, where have you been? Look at your pretty dress. It's all wet and splashed with mud. You know better than to play in the rain. You slipped out without asking me. You left the front door open, and see what has happened. Look at the floor! It is tracked with mud. Tramps came while Cook and I were gone. They stole all the food in the pantry. There isn't a thing left for supper."

"Oh, no," said Louisa, "there weren't any tramps. I gave the food to the children. They were hungry. Oh, Auntie, their mothers were so happy to get the food. It is just the way it is at home. Fathers are out of work. They haven't money to buy enough for their children to eat. Isn't it good that you had enough for all of them?"

"Louisa! What are you saying? Did you

bring children in here from off the street? Did you give them the food from my pantry without asking?"

"They were hungry," said Louisa simply. "You were away." Louisa saw that Auntie was not pleased. She was surprised. At home Father and Mother gave everything away. They laughed and were happy about it.

"I don't know how to punish you for this, Louisa. It is wrong to take food from the pantry without asking permission. You know that."

"We aren't hungry," said Louisa. "It was right to give away the food."

"Don't talk back, Louisa. I said it was wrong to take food without asking. Now you must go to the attic and stay there until you tell me you're sorry."

Louisa went up the stairs. "I'm not sorry," she said to herself. "I'm not sorry." The more she said it the angrier she grew. On the way to the third floor, she stamped her feet on every step. On the way to the attic, she kicked every step. She was acting like a bad-tempered, naughty little girl.

She banged the attic door behind her as hard as she could. It seemed to shake the house. She locked the door. Then she turned and looked around the attic. It didn't look the same now that she was up here by herself. It was a great big attic. There were dark shadows under the eaves. Louisa went over to one of the low windows and opened it. She leaned out far over the sill.

"Oh, oh, oh! I can see the whole world from here. Down there is the lilac bush where I buried Dolly."

Away off were the fields and the woods.

"There's the road where the stagecoach runs. There's the inn. The people look like dwarfs. I can almost see Mother's house!"

Then Louisa was quiet for a while. She was

thinking. She wondered what everybody was doing at home. The sun was low in the west. Father would be coming home. Anna would be helping Mother with supper. Lizzie would be playing with her dolls. Louisa wondered if she would ever see them again. Auntie had said, "Stay there until you tell me you're sorry."

"I'm not sorry, not one bit. I shall stay up here all night." She saw the lights begin to show in the houses below, and the lamps glimmer one by one as the lamplighter made his rounds. She heard mothers call other children in to supper. No one called Louisa.

"Maybe, if I'm never sorry, I'll live up here always. Maybe I'll be like the old woman in the tower in 'Sleeping Beauty.' Maybe everybody will forget that I'm up here."

She began to wish she had not stamped on the stairs. Father and Mother would be unhappy when they heard about that.

She wished she were home. "If ever I get home again, I'm going to be more like Anna. I'm going to do my work and not run away and play all day. It was naughty of me to kick the stairs and lose my temper. I am sorry about that, but not about the food."

It grew dark in the attic. Louisa leaned on the window sill and looked toward home. She blinked hard to keep from crying. "I shall not cry. Auntie will think I'm sorry and I'm not sorry."

All was quiet. The whole city was still. Louisa laid her head on her arms. In a moment she was asleep.

She woke up suddenly. There were voices down below. Auntie and Uncle and Christopher and Ellen and Cook were all talking. Loudest of all was Christopher.

"Mother, Louisa didn't understand," he said. "She imagined you would be pleased because she thought of the other children. They share everything at her home. She didn't stop to think that the food was not hers."

"Oh, the poor little girl!" said Auntie. "No wonder she felt hurt."

"Run quickly, Christopher," said Uncle. "Go to Louisa and tell her we didn't understand about sharing. Tell her we are sorry."

Ellen said, "Tell her I won't say another word about the muddy floors."

Cook said, "I have a little cake that I had tucked away for myself. I'll bring it to her and a glass of milk, bless her little heart."

Louisa heard Christopher running up the stairs. She ran to let him in. He picked her up. She cried and cried. She knew everything was all right, but she cried anyhow. She was sorrier and sorrier that she had acted so ugly coming up the stairs. She told Christopher over and over how sorry she was. Christopher sat down in a lit-

tle old rocking chair that was up in the attic. He
held Louisa in his arms and rocked her. She
cried all her naughtiness away. Finally he took
out his big handkerchief and she wiped her eyes
and blew her nose.

Then they went downstairs together. Every-

She cried all her naughtiness away.

body hugged everybody else and said they were sorry. They all had a little supper in Louisa's room, and Auntie read to her until she went to sleep.

The next morning the sun was shining and the birds were singing. The little girls came with their dolls and fancy hats and dresses. Louisa forgot all the troubles of the day before.

A week later she went home.

She didn't forget what she had thought out in the attic at Auntie's. She didn't run out to play and leave all her work for Anna any more, but swept and dusted and sewed.

Mother was happy to have such a helpful Louisa. Father was proud of his little girl.

"Louisa has changed," said Mother one day. "She's growing into a lovable child."

"Something happened to her while she was away," said the wise father.

Mother wrote a little note in Louisa's diary and told her how pleased they were with her.

XVII

THE ALCOTTS MOVE AGAIN

"I LOVE to move," said Louisa one fine spring day. "Some people I know have lived in the same place for years and years."

"I feel sorry for them," said Anna. "It's so much fun to wake up in a new place."

Anna and Louisa were busy packing while they talked. Lizzie ran back and forth carrying things.

The Alcotts were moving again. They were leaving Boston. Father could find no school. There was no work for him in the city.

"We must go where I can plant a garden," he said. "Then we shall have food even if we have no money."

"I'll be glad to have Louisa out of the crowded city. Where shall we go?" asked Mrs. Alcott.

"Come to Concord," a good friend wrote to

Mr. Alcott. This friend was a very great man. His name was Ralph Waldo Emerson, and he lived in Concord. "It is a good place for children," he said. "My children are happy here. They can run and play without danger. The air is clean and fresh. There are streams, and fields, and forests, and gardens. Best of all, there are many good people. They make fine neighbors."

Mr. Alcott liked Mr. Emerson. He trusted him and listened to his advice.

So the Alcotts moved to Concord. They lived in a pretty cottage at the edge of the village. They loved it.

Father made a large garden at the side of the house. There was an orchard, too. All about them were rolling meadows and forest land, just as Mr. Emerson had said.

The first morning in Concord, before she was really wide awake, Louisa lay listening to the sounds that came through the open windows. She waited to hear the noise of horses' feet, and the racket of wagon wheels rolling over cobblestones. She waited for the *tooot, tooot, tooot* of the steamboats in Boston Bay. Not one of these old sounds did she hear. That made her open her eyes in surprise. Then she remembered. This was Concord.

Strange sounds came from outdoors. Roosters were crowing, birds singing. Louisa took her morning bath, dressed in a hurry, and ran out to see this new country.

It seemed to her that the whole world sparkled like a jewel. She loved to see dew shining on the meadows in the early sunlight. She thought she must be dreaming when she saw the pink apple blossoms and the white cherry and plum blooms. She shut her eyes and pinched herself, then looked again. "I'm awake," she said. "It's all really here."

"I believe you like the country," said a kind voice behind her.

Louisa turned about. Who could this be, up as early as she was? It was Mr. Emerson. Mrs. Emerson was with him. They carried baskets on their arms.

"We've come to have breakfast with you," said Mrs. Emerson. "I know how hard it is to find pots and pans and food after you move, so I brought breakfast with me."

Louisa ran to call Mother. Mother was digging soap and towels out of a barrel and wondering what barrel the breakfast food was in.

"We have company for breakfast," shouted Louisa.

Mother was startled. "Oh dear!" she thought. "Where can we eat? What can we eat? The tables and chairs are covered with packages."

Mr. Emerson and Mr. Alcott carried the table out to the orchard.

Just then Mrs. Emerson came in. "It is so beautiful this morning, Mr. Emerson and I thought we'd share our breakfast with you. Can't we eat out under the apple trees?"

"Let's do, let's do," sang Louisa, who could not bear to come into the house so soon.

Mr. Emerson and Mr. Alcott carried the table out into the orchard. Anna and Louisa gathered apple blossoms. Elizabeth brought a bowl for them and set it on the table. Mrs. Emerson and Mother unpacked the baskets and put the food on the table. What a merry breakfast they had!

Louisa looked up into the blossoms overhead and at the happy faces around her, and cried, "Let's live here always."

XVIII

BUSY DAYS AT CONCORD

THE Alcotts soon had many new friends. The Emersons brought the Hawthornes, who lived quite near. Mr. Hawthorne wrote books. The Goodwins and the Channings came often, too. These people had children, and their children brought others, so Anna and Louisa and Lizzie had lots of new playmates.

They had wonderful times in Concord. The Emerson children showed them where the wild strawberries grew, and where the violets were thickest. The boys pointed out the best trees to climb, and the best pools to fish in.

Louisa liked the woods and hills of Concord better than the streets of Boston. But it was not a very safe place for her.

One day a neighbor came running to Mrs. Alcott.

"Mrs. Alcott, Mrs. Alcott!" she called. "Your little Louisa is going to be killed!"

Mother grew pale. "What has happened? Where is she?"

"In the top of the sycamore tree at the edge of the cliff." The woman pointed. "There's the tree. Can you see her, or has she already fallen?"

Mrs. Alcott saw Louisa high up against the sky. She looked like a tiny speck so far above the ground. Louisa caught sight of Mother, and took off her sunbonnet and waved.

Mother untied her apron and waved it back.

"Louisa will be all right," she said to the well-meaning neighbor. "She's used to climbing, and the wind and sunlight are good for her." The neighbor went away shaking her head. She was not so sure.

Mother would not have been so sure, either, if she had heard what the boys were saying. They were at the foot of the tree watching Louisa. "She's climbing too high," said Tom. "The branches won't hold her. Doesn't she know any better?"

"I dared her to go to the top," said Cy, "and she'll do it."

"What if it breaks with her? Tell her to come down." Louisa was already at the top. "Look at me! Look at me! I did it." Just then there was a loud crack!

"Come down! Come down!" screamed the boys. Louisa teased them. She swayed in the creaking treetop until she tired of it; then she climbed down.

"Let's go fishing," suggested Frank, when Louisa was safe on the ground.

"I want to go, too," said Louisa.

"Girls can't fish. They're afraid of fishing worms."

"I'm not."

"You'll cry if you hook a fish."

"I won't either. I'm not a crybaby."

"I can make you cry."

"No, you can't."

"I'll show you. Come here. Hold out your hands." Louisa held them out. Frank had a book strap hidden in his pocket. He whipped it out and lashed it across the backs of Louisa's hands. Tom and Cy cried out in anger and snatched the strap away from him and chased him home, giving him a taste of his own medicine every step of the way.

Louisa followed at their heels. "It didn't hurt. It didn't hurt," she shouted. "Only let me go fishing with you."

It wasn't long before all the boys knew that Louisa couldn't resist a dare. It came to be a kind of game to find something new for her to try.

"I dare you to jump the fence," cried one.

"I dare you to chew tobacco," teased another.

"I dare you to rub pepper in your eyes!"

Louisa took every dare. Mother was at her wits' ends. Every day Louisa came home bruised, or sick, or nearly blind. "Why *won't* you play with your doll again and forget the boys and their rough play?"

"Dolls aren't exciting. Boys have so much more fun than girls."

A day came, though, when Louisa had to be quiet. She and Cy were playing in the barn. Cy was her favorite playmate, because his dares were always dangerous and she never knew how they were going to come out. Cy climbed into the haymow and walked out across a beam high above the floor. Louisa followed close behind him.

"I dare you to drop," he called over his shoulder.

Louisa dropped. She was badly hurt, with

Louisa followed close behind him.

both ankles sprained, and had to stay in bed for
days and days.

At first the children stopped in to visit her and
brought her presents, like kittens and turtles.
But after a while they forgot her. Mother and

Anna were too busy to read to her. She was tired and lonely.

Mother felt sorry for the little prisoner. She brought her a pencil and some paper. "Why don't you write a little story or play for me? It will help you pass the time."

"I'll write out one of the plays Anna and I used to give in the evenings in Boston," said Louisa. Soon she was scribbling away at a great rate.

When the play was finished, Mother and Father read it and thought it was as good as some grownups could write. "Copy this, Louisa," said Father. "Spell it correctly and write it neatly." Louisa did as he told her. "Keep on writing. Finish each play or story or poem carefully. Perhaps some day you'll write a real book."

XIX

PLAY DAYS AT CONCORD

TIME flew by. The Alcotts were poor, but the children didn't mind. They were as happy as they could be. They had the woods and the meadows and the orchard to play in.

Behind the Alcott cottage was a fine, big barn. The girls took this for their playhouse. They could do just as they pleased there, and not bother anybody.

"This will be just the place to give our plays in," said Louisa. She climbed up the ladder into the hayloft.

"We can act out *Jack and the Beanstalk!*" she shouted. "The giant can fall out of the hayloft."

"Oh, what fun!" cried Anna. "Jack can climb up the ladder to the giant's castle and steal the goose that lays the golden egg."

"We can cover the ladder with a vine, so it will

look like a beanstalk. Let's get to work on it
right away."

They swept out the barn and moved everything out of the way. Some of their friends came
in to play. Louisa set them to work. The boys
dragged in part of an old chicken house, and
Louisa had them paint it. They propped it up
with the bran box. "Now it looks like the cottage
that Jack and his mother lived in," they said.

"We need a long vine to cover the ladder. Is
there a wild grapevine near here?" asked Louisa.

"That won't look like a beanstalk," the boys
said.

"I know what we can use. We'll get a squash
vine."

"Hurrah!" cried the boys. "We know where
to get plenty. They grow along the fences everywhere."

"Be sure to ask first," said Anna, "and don't

leave any squashes on the vine. That would give the whole thing away."

"A squash would be an awfully big bean, wouldn't it?"

Before the children could work more on the play, it was suppertime. They decided not to tell their parents.

"It will be a surprise."

Louisa was so full of plans for the next day that she didn't know what she was doing that evening. After the dishes were washed, she put her pencil and slate in the cupboard and carried the bread and butter into the living room. She emptied the sugar bowl into the salt box.

"You need a guardian," giggled Anna. "You must be more careful or Mother will suspect something."

That evening, to please Louisa, Father read the story about the old woman who had three wishes. Anna and Louisa knew it by heart. He came to the part where the old woman wishes the pudding were on the end of her husband's nose. Louisa cried out, "We can act that out easily. We'll let the pudding down on a string from the hayloft."

"Louisa!" shrieked Anna. "You're telling." Louisa clapped her hand over her mouth.

Mother and Father didn't seem to notice.

The children of the neighborhood were as busy as bees the next few days. They made the costumes for the play in the barn so that the grownups wouldn't guess what was going on.

Louisa was the giant. She wore one of Father's old coats. They had stuffed it with padding from a carriage cushion. She practiced falling out of the hayloft. She fell "ker-spling, ker-splung." The boys and girls shouted and clapped. "That will be the funniest part of the play," they said.

Finally everything was ready. All the children wrote invitations to their parents. "Come to the Alcotts' barn at four o'clock today," they said.

The mothers of the neighborhood hurried through their work. The fathers came home early. All of them went to the barn.

Little Lizzie met them at the door. She led them to their seats—boards laid across saw horses. A curtain hung down from the rafters at one end of the barn. It was made of many old coverlets sewed together. Nearly every family recognized parts of it.

The curtain went up. There was a loud thud. The curtain came down. The parents heard scurrying feet. The chicken house had fallen down. The boys raised it up and two of them stood behind it and held it up.

Then the curtain went up again. Everything was all right this time. The squash vine looked like a beanstalk at the side of the house. Jack climbed up it. He came scrambling down with

All the parents were invited to see the play.

a squawking hen under his arm. Something happened that Jack wasn't expecting. The hen took that moment to lay a real egg. Everybody laughed. "I thought she was supposed to lay golden eggs," someone said. The play went on. Jack chopped down the beanstalk. Down tumbled Mr. Giant, bumpety-bump, and the play was over.

The parents clapped and clapped. They waited to see if the giant were really killed. "Give more plays," they said. "We like them."

All summer and fall Anna and Louisa were busy with their plays. Louisa wrote them and Anna helped with the costumes. All the children made the scenery and took parts. Once they gave *Cinderella*. Louisa made a great big pumpkin for her to ride away in.

No wonder Louisa and Anna didn't notice how poor they were. They were so busy they didn't even see how hard Father and Mother worked.

XX

THE GREAT PLAN

ANOTHER baby girl was born in the Alcott cottage. Her name was Abba May. She was like a live doll, with golden hair and pink cheeks.

The cottage was crowded. Anna and Lizzie and Louisa slept in one room. It was fun, but Louisa wanted a room of her own. She liked to write her plays at night, but she couldn't do that now, because Anna and Lizzie couldn't sleep with a light on. It was hard to write in the daytime when there were so many people around.

Mother was busy with the baby, and Anna and Louisa had to help with the cooking and ironing and sewing. They hurried as fast as they could with their tasks so that they could play in the barn.

There was another important event. Father

went to England. He was gone a long time. Louisa did the heavy chores about the house. She carried the buckets of water from the well, and filled the wood-box, and tended the garden. She was quite strong now, and big for her age, and liked the hard work much better than the sewing and ironing.

When Father came home, he brought some strangers with him, Mr. Wright and Mr. Lane and his son. The cottage was already so full that Louisa said, "I don't see where we're going to put everybody." But Mother managed somehow. She always did.

Nothing was the same in the cottage after Mr. Lane came. He and Father talked together all the time, or went to Mr. Emerson's and talked. Many strange people came to visit. They stayed on, and so the cottage was still more crowded, and Mother and the girls cooked day and night to prepare enough food for all of them.

Everybody talked a great deal. It was very tiresome.

"Why don't you read to us any more, Father? Why don't you send these queer people away?" asked Louisa one day.

"They are not queer, Louisa. They are great thinkers and teachers."

"What do you talk about all the time?"

"Mr. Lane and I wish to try out a wonderful plan. These others are interested, too. They may try it with us."

"What is the plan?"

"It's about a new way of living. You know how poor everyone is, and how there is no work in the cities. Our plan is to go to the country. We shall buy a big farm and live without cities. We shall do everything with our own hands."

"Where will we get goods to make our clothes? Where will you get a plow? Where will sugar come from?"

"We shall raise flax. Linen comes from flax. We'll make our clothes from that. I shall make my own plow. And sugar comes from sugar cane."

"Will the farm have a house large enough for all of us?"

"Yes, a great big house."

"Then I'm ready to go," said Louisa. "I'm tired of the crowded cottage."

"I don't want to leave Concord," said Anna. "This has been the best home in our whole lives."

"I shall miss the barn and all our friends, too," said Louisa, "but I want more room."

Spring had come again before the plan was worked out. Finally Father and Mr. Lane and a few teachers were ready to try it. They bought a farm. It had a big, empty house on it. "It is old, but I can fix it up," said Father.

Father was a good carpenter and farmer.

Many people made fun of the plan. "It won't work," they said.

"Father can do anything," said Louisa. "He can make the plan work."

"Be ready to start in a few days," he said at last.

Mother began to pack. Once more the Alcotts were moving.

XXI

A DREARY JOURNEY

MOVING day came. Louisa stood in the door of the cottage at Concord and looked out. It was early morning.

"It's raining cats and dogs," she told Anna.

"I suppose it will keep on all day," said Anna. "It will be cold riding in the open wagon."

"Who minds a little cold water?" scoffed Louisa. "We must see that Mother and Baby are warm. The rest of us will be all right."

Anna hoped that Father would put off moving. She hoped the wagon wouldn't come. But the wagon came. All their belongings were piled into it.

There was only one umbrella. Mother took Abba May on her lap and held the umbrella over her. The furniture and food were covered with

Mother took Abba May on her lap and held the umbrella over her.

heavy canvas. The men held heavy brown wrapping paper over their heads and shoulders.

Louisa liked starting off in the rain. "It makes it more exciting," she said. "This is an adventure." She put her arms around Anna to warm her. "We'll crawl under the canvas," she said. "That will keep us dry."

"Let's talk about when we grow up," said Anna. "I'm going to be a great actress."

"I shall write plays and act them," said Louisa.
"I'm going to make a lot of money."

"Then Father can have a fine pair of boots and
a warm coat."

"And Mother won't have to ride in the cold
and wet," added Louisa. "Oh, it seems so long
to wait to grow up. I wish we were rich right
now."

All day they traveled. The wagon jolted along
the muddy, hilly road. It rained and rained.
Even Louisa was cold and wet and tired.

It was nearly sundown when the horses turned
up a steep hill. Father came running to the side
of the wagon. He had walked all the way.

"We're here!" he shouted. "We're here!"

Anna and Louisa tumbled out from under the
canvas. They saw a big, deserted old farmhouse.
The wagon stopped at the door. Just then the
sun came out. A great rainbow spread across

the eastern sky. Louisa stood up in the wagon. She looked out over the hills and valleys.

"What a wonderful place to play in!" she thought.

XXII

FRUITLANDS

THE new home was called Fruitlands. The house looked lonely and dirty the night they moved in. It was different in a few days. Mother had it clean and shining. Pretty rugs were on the floor, bright flowers on the table, and a cheery fire burned in the fireplace.

There was little time for play at Fruitlands. All the food had to be raised on the farm. Nothing was bought at a grocery or bakery. Father worked early and late in the fields. Mother baked from morning till night. It took a lot of bread to feed all the teachers and children.

Father came in late from the fields one night. He was tired and discouraged. "The corn is ready to husk, but we haven't enough workers," he said.

"Then the girls and I shall help," said Mother.

"Tomorrow, you shall have three new helpers."

The next morning Mother flew around. "The housework must be done before noon," she said, "for we will start husking after dinner."

Anna and Louisa helped Mother instead of having their lessons. This pleased them. Mr.

It was hard work.

Lane was their teacher at Fruitlands, and they didn't like him.

After dinner they hurried to the barn. Father showed them how to strip the husks off the ears.

Everybody went to work—the teachers, Father, Mother and the children. It was hard work. Anna's and Louisa's hands were stiff and sore. Their backs ached, but they worked on.

"It will soon be suppertime," said Mother. "Shall we bring the supper out here to the barn?"

"Yes, yes," voted everybody. One of the men carried the big iron kettle from the house. It was full of hot, savory vegetable soup. Anna and Louisa brought the loaves of bread that Mother had baked. Father hung up lanterns, so that they could see to eat. They threw a pretty light on the piles of golden corn.

After supper Mother took Lizzie and Abba May to bed. Anna and Louisa were allowed to stay and husk as long as they could keep awake.

The sun went down. The stars came out. Father built a fire outside the barn. They sat around the fire and went on working. Someone began a song. Everybody joined in. They sang all the rest of the evening, until the last ear of corn was husked.

Anna and Louisa were so sleepy that they fairly tumbled into bed.

The moon shone in on Louisa late in the night. It woke her up. She thought about the corn husking.

"That is the best time we have had since we came to Fruitlands."

XXIII

THE BARLEY AND THE STORM

"I AM going for a good, long run," said Louisa. It was a bright, frosty morning. The Alcotts had been at Fruitlands several months. "Mr. Lane and Father are away, so we won't have lessons."

She ran over the hills up to the highest point. She liked to stretch out under the pine trees there. It was almost always quiet and peaceful.

Today it was different. The wind roared through the branches. In the valley it was warm. On the hilltop it was too cold for Louisa. She ran back down the long slope to the farmhouse.

"Mother, it's turning cold."

Mother went out to the brow of the hill. She looked worried. There were dark clouds in the north.

158

"If it snows, the barley will be lost," she said. "It has been cut, but not gathered."

The wind blew colder. The clouds shut out the sun.

"Children," she called, "there's not a moment to lose. We must gather in the grain. The men will not return in time."

"How can we, Mother? We haven't a wagon or anything to put it in."

"We'll do the way the women did in Bible times. They carried the grain in their aprons. I'll give each of you one of mine." They all tied on the big aprons, even little Lizzie. Hers dragged on the ground, so Mother fastened it around her neck. Then Mother brought out her biggest sheets. They were of very heavy linen and had been made in Russia. She spread them on the ground.

"Fill your aprons with the barley as fast as you can," she ordered her little army. "Then

They worked as hard and fast as they could.

empty them into the sheets. When the sheets are full, we'll drag them to the barn and empty the grain on the floor, then come back for more. Hurry, hurry, hurry."

They worked as hard and fast as they could. The wind blew colder. The clouds were black. Slowly the pile of grain grew on the barn floor. The children's feet were bleeding. The sharp stubble cut through their shoes. Their arms ached. Their legs seemed made of wood, they were so tired.

"Keep on a little longer, my brave soldiers," encouraged Mother. "We are nearly finished."

All of them together dragged the last sheet into the barn. The storm came. It was a blizzard. They ran for the house. They couldn't see. The snow blinded them. The wind sucked their breath away. Mother carried Lizzie so she wouldn't be lost. "Hold onto my apron strings," she called to Anna and Louisa. "It is easy to lose your way in a storm like this."

They reached the house safely. Mother built up the fire. She bathed the children's feet and wrapped them in soft linen.

"Father will be proud of you," she said, while she worked. "You have saved the food for the winter."

Father came home the next morning. He had traveled all night. He saw the fields covered with snow and said sadly, "We shall have to go back to the city. There will be no food here. The barley is buried in snow."

Mother said, "Come with me to the barn." When he saw the barley, safely harvested, he looked at her in wonder. "How did you do it?" he asked. She told him all that had happened.

He went back to the house and called the children to him. He put his arms around them and said a little prayer. He thanked God that his children were safe, and thanked Him for their brave and wonderful mother.

XXIV

FAREWELL TO FRUITLANDS

THE winter was long and cold at Fruitlands. Mr. Lane was discouraged. He didn't like the cold and grew tired of the plain food. One morning he went away and didn't come back. He took his son with him. The other teachers also left.

Anna and Louisa were glad. "I like to have just our family here," Louisa said. "I wish we could always have just us."

Father was very sad. "We cannot make the great plan work if people run away when they are discouraged," he said. He worried so much about it that he grew ill. He couldn't eat. Finally he was so weak that he had to go to bed.

One night Mother came to the bed where Anna and Louisa were sleeping. "Wake up!" she whispered. "Get up and dress. Don't make any noise. We mustn't disturb your father. Come to the barn where we can talk."

They dressed as quickly as their shaking hands would let them. They tiptoed out of the house and ran to the barn.

"What is it, Mother? What's the matter?"

"We must leave Fruitlands at once," she said. "I have been through the grain box and the flour bin and the apple cellar. There's not enough food for another day.

"Father is not well enough to travel, but we shall starve if we stay. Louisa, get out the bobsled that Father made in Concord. Nail longer boards onto it. We shall use it like a sleigh. Anna and I will make it soft with pillows and blankets. The three of us can lift Father onto it. We shall pull Father on the sled to our nearest friends', the Lovejoys. We must start as soon as we can, for it feels like rain. If it rains, the snow will melt. Then we couldn't move, for the sled would be too heavy, and the roads would be too soft for a wagon."

A little before daylight they were ready. Louisa made the sled into a sleigh. Then she rubbed soap on the runners and brought it to Father's bedside. "The soap will make it slide over the floor easily. We can lift Father onto it here."

Mother and Anna piled the sled with warm blankets. It was no trouble to lift Father; he had grown so thin. Then each took up a small bundle, and they were ready to move. They put Lizzie in the sleigh, too. This time Father carried Abba May.

It was a heavy load and they pulled it a long way. They were very tired, and it began to rain.

"It's the same sort of rain we started to Fruitlands in," said Louisa, "but everything else is different. Father's sick. Our dear, brave mother looks old and tired. I'm different, too."

Anna began to cry. "You sound so sad."

"I'm not sad, Anna. I'm just growing up. I'm not twelve yet, but I feel old. I'm going to try with all my might to take care of my family. Some day, I'm going to make you all rich and comfortable."

"You're always saying that," said Anna.

"I'm always dreaming about it, too."

It was a heavy load and

It was getting harder and harder to pull the
sled. Then Louisa saw the Lovejoys' house
through the rain.

They hurried as fast as they could.

Mr. Lovejoy saw them coming. He threw
open the door. People ran out, calling "Welcome, welcome." They carried Father into the
house. They made a place for Mother by the

they pulled it a long way.

fire, and brought heaping plates of food to all
the family.

How good it was to be among friends again!

XXV

ANNA AND LOUISA GO TO WORK

I T WAS a long time before the Alcotts had a home of their own again. They had no money. Father was too weak to work. Kind friends made room for them in their homes, but they were always crowded.

"It is dreadful to be poor," whispered Anna to Louisa one night. "People are talking about Father. They laugh at him behind his back and say, 'Mr. Alcott and his big ideas!' I can't bear it."

"We must find a way to make money," said Louisa. "If we were rich, people would believe in Father."

"But how can we make money? We're only little girls."

"Mr. Emerson will help us," said Louisa suddenly. "We can teach his little children the way

Father taught us. He knows what a great man Father is.

"We could have a school for younger children in Mr. Emerson's barn."

"We can help Mrs. Emerson with her sewing, too. I can sew well," added Anna proudly.

The two girls went to the Emersons' the first thing the next morning. They told them their plans.

"This is splendid," said Mr. Emerson. "You may begin at once."

"I need Anna to help with my sewing today," said Mrs. Emerson. "If Louisa will teach our younger children and the Goodwins' and Channings' each morning, the mothers will be glad to pay her every week."

So Louisa and Anna went to work. They didn't earn enough to rent a house, but they were busy and much happier.

In the afternoons they took care of Lizzie and

Abba May. Anna made Lizzie's dolls new dresses from scraps Mrs. Emerson gave her. Louisa made them fancy hats.

"Why, Louisa, those are the most stylish hats I ever saw. I didn't know you could do anything like that," said Anna.

"I didn't either," replied Louisa.

Lizzie's little playmates saw the hats. "Please make us some, Louisa. We'll pay for them."

"Why, that will be fun. It seems odd to be paid for having fun." Louisa made them many hats, but they wanted more and more of them. She printed a little sign and put it in the window. "Doll hats made to order."

It wasn't long before she had more orders than she could fill. She had a hard time finding enough material.

"Make mine with feathers on it," said one little girl.

"I haven't any more feathers," said Louisa.

The child was unhappy. "I did so want one like Lizzie's."

Another little girl said, "I did, too. It would look so elegant with my doll's new dress."

"Then I must get some more feathers," said Louisa. She went up and down the streets. The children followed her. She came to a back yard where there were chickens. She pointed at them. "There are some feathers," she said.

"But how can you get them?" The girls were disappointed.

"I'll show you," said Louisa. She jumped over the fence into the chicken lot. She grabbed at a red hen. The hen was fat. She waddled. She couldn't run fast. Louisa easily caught her and pulled out some of her downy feathers. What a fuss the hen made!

"Those feathers will make very fashionable hats," cried the girls joyously.

"I wish you could get some white feathers for

She grabbed at a red hen.

my doll's hat," said one. "They would look so nice with her white satin cloak."

"Perhaps we can find some white hens," said Louisa. They all ran up and down the streets till they found some white hens. Louisa chased them and pulled feathers with both hands. The little girls stood on the outside of the fence screaming, "Get me one out of that hen. Get me one, get me one." The hens inside the fence set up a loud squawking.

People ran out of their houses to see what was going on. They thought, "Chicken thieves must be after our hens." When they saw Louisa climbing over their fences, chasing roosters and hens, and pulling out their tail feathers, they grabbed their brooms and started after her.

"Who is that dreadful child?" they shouted. They threw sticks at her. Louisa and the other girls ran home as fast as they could go.

They slipped into the house as quiet as mice, and spent the rest of the day making hats.

The summer passed quickly.

"We still haven't enough money," sighed Louisa one night. She and Anna had been counting up their earnings for the summer. "I did so want to buy Mother a new dress and a warm shawl."

"I wish there were some way that we could help Mother," said Anna earnestly. "It must be very hard for her to have to live in other people's houses."

"We must keep 'working and hoping.' That is what she tells us to do. Perhaps, some day, times will be better."

XXVI

A WISH COMES TRUE

TIMES really did get better for the Alcotts. Father grew well and strong again. Mother's father left her some money, enough to buy a house in Concord. It was old and run-down, but Father made a beautiful home of it. How happy Anna and Louisa were! They scoured and cleaned the old walls and floors. They papered and painted and polished.

One of the first things Father did was to build an extra room on to the house. It had big windows and a door opening onto a pretty garden. Mother had a nice desk put in it, and comfortable chairs. She made bright-colored rugs for the floor and white ruffled curtains for the windows. In the closet she hid sweet-smelling herbs.

"This is the sweetest room that ever was," said Louisa, when everything was finished.

"I can write plays and stories whenever I wish."

177

"We are glad you like it," said Father and Mother smilingly, "for it is yours, Louisa."

"Mine!" gasped Louisa. "I've wanted a room like this all my life."

"You have been patient and kind, and have worked hard. You have earned this room. You will enjoy it more now that you deserve it."

"Surely I shall never be unhappy again," cried Louisa. "I can write plays and stories whenever I wish."

XXVII

A HAPPY ENDING

Y EARS passed. Anna and Louisa were young
ladies, beautiful and popular. They were
asked to all the gay parties and balls. But they
didn't go. They didn't have anything to wear,
and they were too busy. The Alcotts were
poor again. Father and Mother both worked.
Anna and Louisa taught school in the winter
and took positions as governesses during the
summer. Still there wasn't enough money for
party dresses and good times. Lizzie and Abba
May were growing up. They needed shoes and
clothes.

"I don't know what is going to become of us,"
sighed Anna. "All we do is work. I would love
to have a little fun like other girls before I grow
old."

"Don't give up hope," laughed Louisa. "I still

think that I shall make our fortunes." Anna only smiled sadly. She had heard this before.

Then one day Louisa said, "I am going to Boston. I know that I can make money by writing if I only dare to try."

Mother and Father said, "You are right, Louisa."

Father went up to the attic and brought down Louisa's little old, worn trunk. It was the same trunk that had gone with her to Providence when she was a little girl. Mother and Anna mended and cleaned and pressed Louisa's shabby clothes and folded them neatly into the trunk. Louisa put her pencils and paper and books into it. Lizzie tucked in a shawl that she had knitted herself. "You can wear this on cold nights when you are writing," she said. Abba May gave her some pictures. "Here are sketches I drew. I shall illustrate your books for you," she promised.

The day came for Louisa to leave. The drayman called for her trunk. Louisa set out for the station. At the corner she turned and waved to Father and Mother and Anna and Lizzie and Abba May.

The townspeople shook their heads. "What are the Alcotts thinking of, sending a young lady alone to the city!" "I'd rather see my daughter dead and in her grave," said one. "She'll come running back soon enough," said another. "Whoever heard of a girl making a living by writing!"

Louisa didn't make her living by writing, at first. She sewed for friends and relatives in Boston. Hour after hour she hemmed sheets and blankets and pillow slips. Day after day she sewed ruffles on ball dresses for other young ladies. But while she sewed, she planned her stories, and at night she wrote them.

Finally her stories began to sell. People stopped at bookstores and inquired, "Have you more stories by Louisa May Alcott?" "Do you have a book by Miss Alcott?"

When they passed her on the street, people turned to look after her. "There goes Miss Alcott, the authoress. Isn't she interesting? Isn't she charming?"

Then the Civil War broke out. "We need nurses! We need nurses!" came the cry from the battle fronts. "The wounded are dying like flies because there is no one to care for them."

Louisa left Boston and went back home to Father and Mother. "There are no sons to go to war in our family," she said, "but I am young and strong and would make a good nurse. I know that brave young men are dying and that I might save them. I feel I must go."

"Go, and Godspeed," said Father and Mother.

Again Louisa set out alone. Again the people shook their heads. "Is it true that Louisa is going to serve as a nurse? How can the Alcotts let their daughter go into such danger? The hospitals are full of every kind of disease. They are filthy and overcrowded. She is going to her death."

The hospitals were worse even than Louisa had heard. When she saw the dirty beds and floors, and the poor, unwashed soldiers, she called for buckets of water. She scrubbed and scoured and cleaned. She helped the doctors as they labored over the wounded. She cheered the sick and comforted the dying. People began to hear about her—"Brave, strong, cheerful Louisa."

Then one night Father received a telegram. Louisa was very ill. They thought she was dying. She had worked too hard without rest and good food and fresh air.

Father went to the hospital and brought her home. She didn't know anybody, not even Father or Mother. She was ill a long, long time, but she didn't die. She recovered and began to write again.

She wrote a book that she called *Little Women*. It was about her own family. "Maybe there are other people who have had the same kinds of troubles we have had," she thought. "Maybe there is another little tomboy like me some place, who will like to hear about the scrapes I got into when I was little. Who knows but that the book may help her?"

An invalid friend took her to Europe as her companion soon after the book was finished. She was gone several months. When the ship that brought her home pulled up to the dock in New York, she saw great crowds of people. They were all cheering. Bands were playing. "There must be some famous person on this boat," she said to herself. "It is strange that I didn't hear of it." She saw Father waiting for her, but there was such a throng about her that she couldn't get to him.

All at once she heard people shouting her name. Young people were handing open books to her, saying, "Won't you autograph my book, Miss Alcott?" "Please write your name in mine, Miss Alcott!"

Louisa looked about her in astonishment. She took one of the books and turned it over to see what it was. It was a copy of *Little Women*. Louisa was the famous person everyone had come to see!

Never again did the Alcotts have to worry about the rent, or clothes, or food or doctor bills. Louisa's books were read all over the world. She was rich. She bought her family everything that their hearts could desire. But money and fame did not change her. She shared with others all the good things of her life. The lessons she had learned as a little girl were not forgotten.